Audition Songs for Female Singers 4

I Don't Know How To Love Him...

plus nine more essential audition standards

Wise Publications
London/New York/Paris/Sydney/Copenhagen/Madrid

Other titles in this series...

Audition Songs for Female Singers 1

Don't Cry For Me Argentina...

plus Adelaide's Lament, Big Spender; Heaven Help My Heart; I Cain't Say No; I Will Survive; Out Here On My Own; Saving All My Love For You; Someone To Watch Over Me; The Wind Beneath My Wings. ORDER NO. AM92587

Audition Songs for Female Singers 2

I Dreamed A Dream...

plus Another Suitcase In Another Hall; Fame; If I Were A Bell; Miss Byrd; Save The Best For Last; Someone Else's Story; There Are Worse Things I Could Do; What I Did For Love; You Can Always Count On Me. ORDER NO. AM950224

Audition Songs for Female Singers 3

Memory...

plus Can't Help Lovin' Dat Man; Crazy; Diamonds Are A Girl's Best Friend; Now That I've Seen Her; Show Me Heaven; That Ole Devil Called Love; The Winner Takes It All; Wishing You Were Somehow Here Again; The Reason. ORDER NO. AM955284

Audition Songs for Male Singers 1

Tonight...

plus All Good Gifts; Anthem; Being Alive; Corner Of The Sky; Funny; High Flying, Adored; If I Loved You; Luck Be A Lady; Why, God, Why? ORDER NO. AM92586

Audition Songs for Male Singers 2

Maria...

plus All I Need Is The Girl; Bring Him Home; Frederick's Aria; I Don't Remember Christmas; Sit Down, You're Rocking The Boat; Some Enchanted Evening; This Is The Moment; Where I Want To Be; You're Nothing Without Me. ORDER NO. AM950213

Exclusive Distributors:
Music Sales Limited
8/9 Frith Street,
London W1V 5TZ, England.
Music Sales Pty Limited
120 Rothschild Avenue,
Rosebery, NSW 2018,
Australia.

Order No. AM955295
ISBN 0-7119-7456-X

Compiled by Paul Honey and Nick Crispin
Music arrangements by Paul Honey
Music processed by Enigma Music Production Services

CD performed and recorded by Paul Honey

Book design by Studio Twenty, London

Constant Craving

Words & Music by k.d. lang & Ben Mink

Cm7
D♭/E♭
D♭
Fm7
Cm7
-ways some-one march - es brave, here be-neath my
D♭/E♭
D♭maj/E♭
D♭
E♭/D♭
A♭maj7
skin. And con - - - stant crav - - -
Fm
D♭/G♭
G♭
Fm
-ing has al - - ways been.
E♭/D♭
D♭
A♭
E♭/D♭
Crav - - ing. Ah ha, con-stant crav - -

D♭
E♭
D♭
-ing has al - - - - ways been, has
E♭
D♭
al - - - - - ways been. And
D♭
E♭/D♭
A♭maj7
Fm
con - - - stant crav - - - ing has
D♭/G♭
G♭
Fm
al - - - ways been.

Verse 2:
Maybe a great magnet pulls
All souls towards the truth.
Or maybe it is life itself,
That feeds wisdom to its youth.

As Long As He Needs Me

Words & Music by Lionel Bart

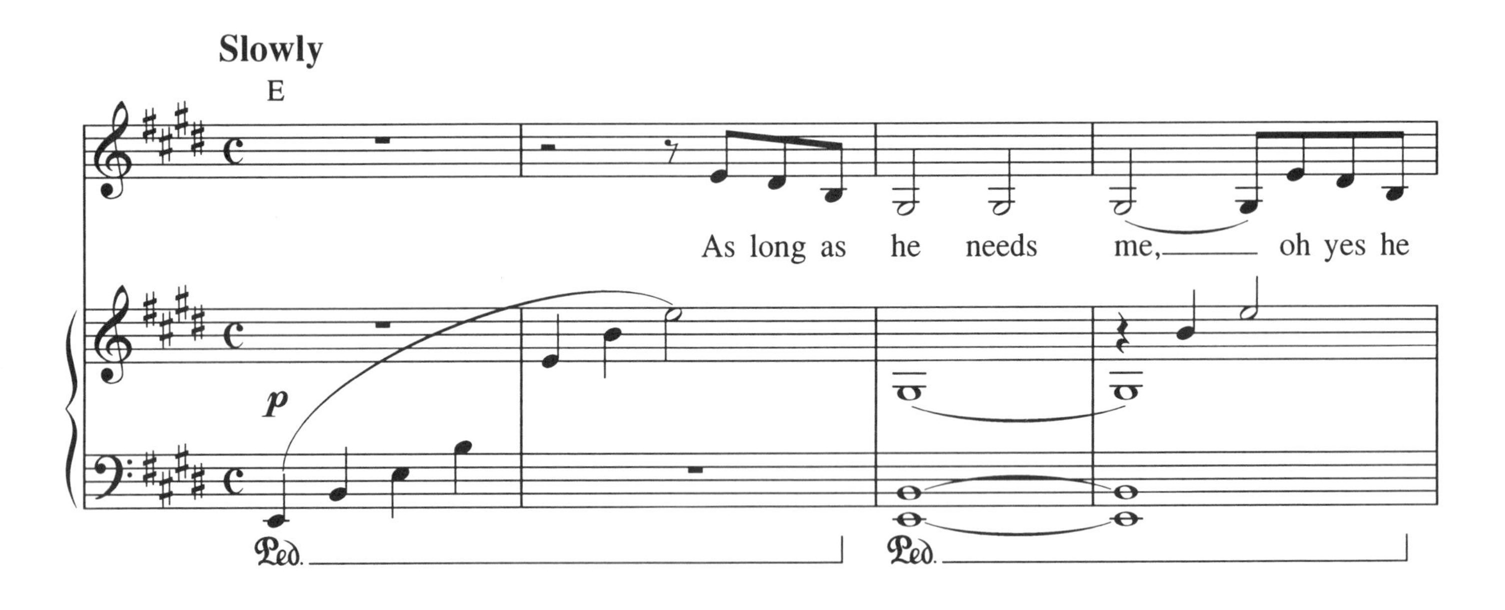

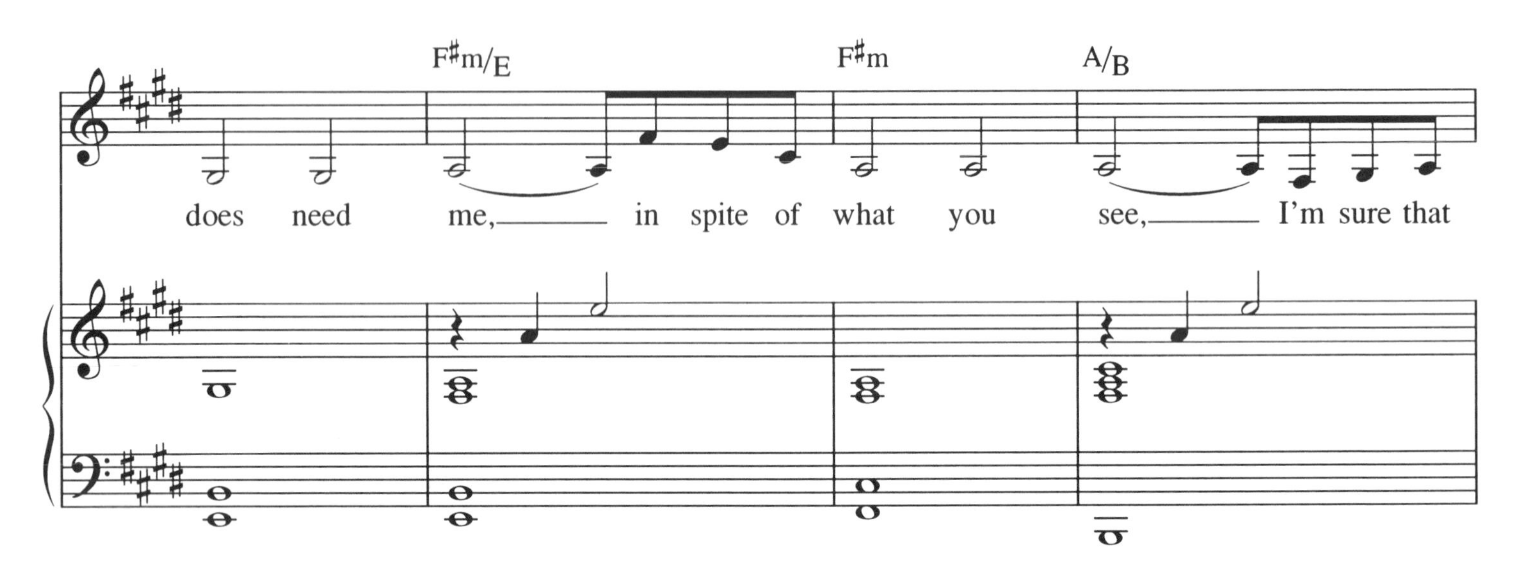

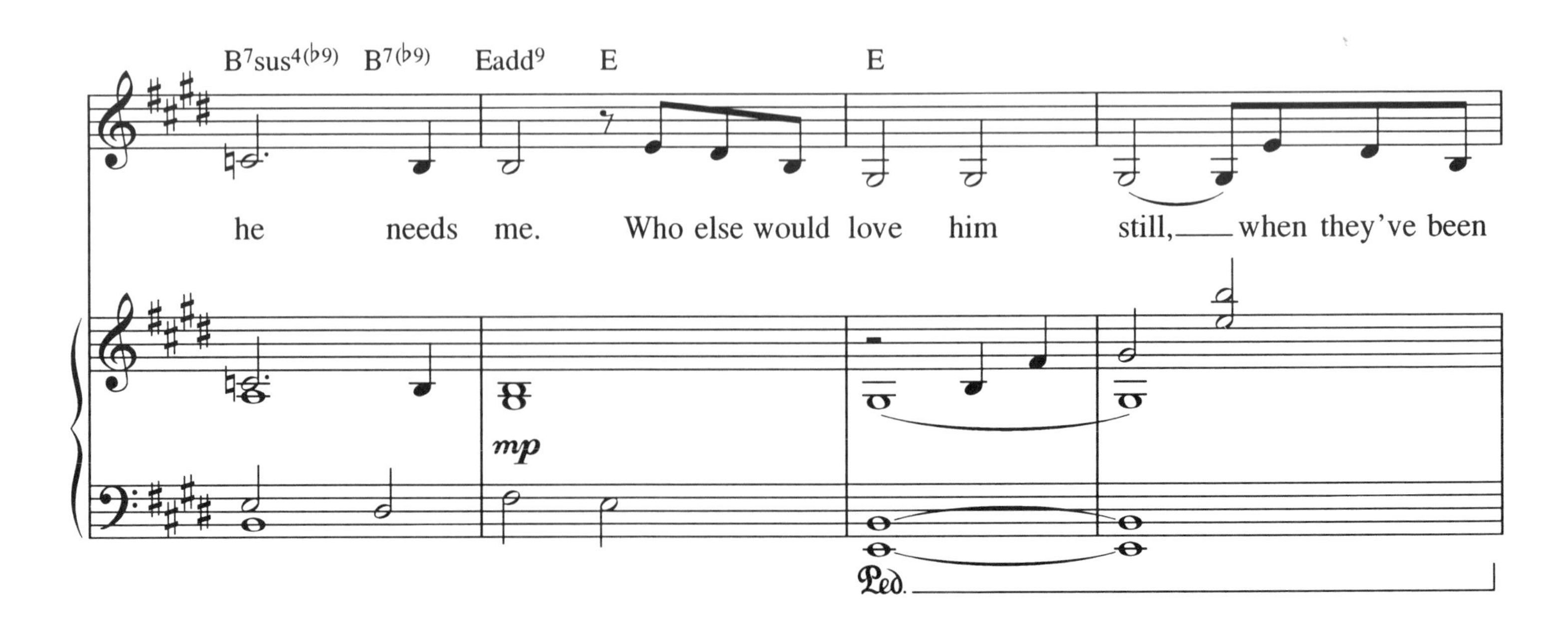

Fdim
F♯m
F♯m7
B7sus4
used so ill? He knows I al - ways will, as long as
espress.
F♯m7(♭5)
Bsus4 B
E
3
Con moto
Fdim
F♯m
B7sus4 B7
E
he needs me. I miss him so much when he is gone.
p
poco rall.
G♯m7/D♯
C♯m7
F♯7
B13
B7sus4
B7
But when he's near me, I don't let on. The way I
Tempo I
Eadd9
E
Fdim
F♯m7
feel in - side, the love I have to hide, the hell! I've
mp
Ped.

Amaj7 F#7sus4/C# F#7 F#m7 B7(♭9) E
got my pride, as long as he needs me.
Con moto
E/B Bdim A/B F#m7/B B7(♭9) Am/E E
He does-n't say the things he should, he acts the way he thinks he should.
mf
C#m7 G#m7 C#9 F#9 F#m/B
rall.
But all the same I'll play this game his way.
a tempo
B7 Eadd9 E Fdim
As long as he needs me, I know where I must
mp

F♯m
D/F
B⁹
Am/B
B
be, I'll cling on stead - fast - - ly, as long as he needs
poco più mosso
E
E
Fdim
me. As long as life is long, I'll love him right or
mf
F♯m⁷
D/F♯
B⁹
B⁷(♭9)
wrong, and some-how I'll be strong as long as he needs
Con moto
E
3
Fdim
B⁹/F♯
Eadd⁹/G♯
A⁶
me. If you are lone - ly, then you will know when some-one
cresc.

molto rall.
E/B
F♯7/C♯
Am6/E
D7
needs you, you love them so. I won't be -

a tempo
G
G♯dim
Am7
- tray his trust, though peo - ple say I must, I've got to

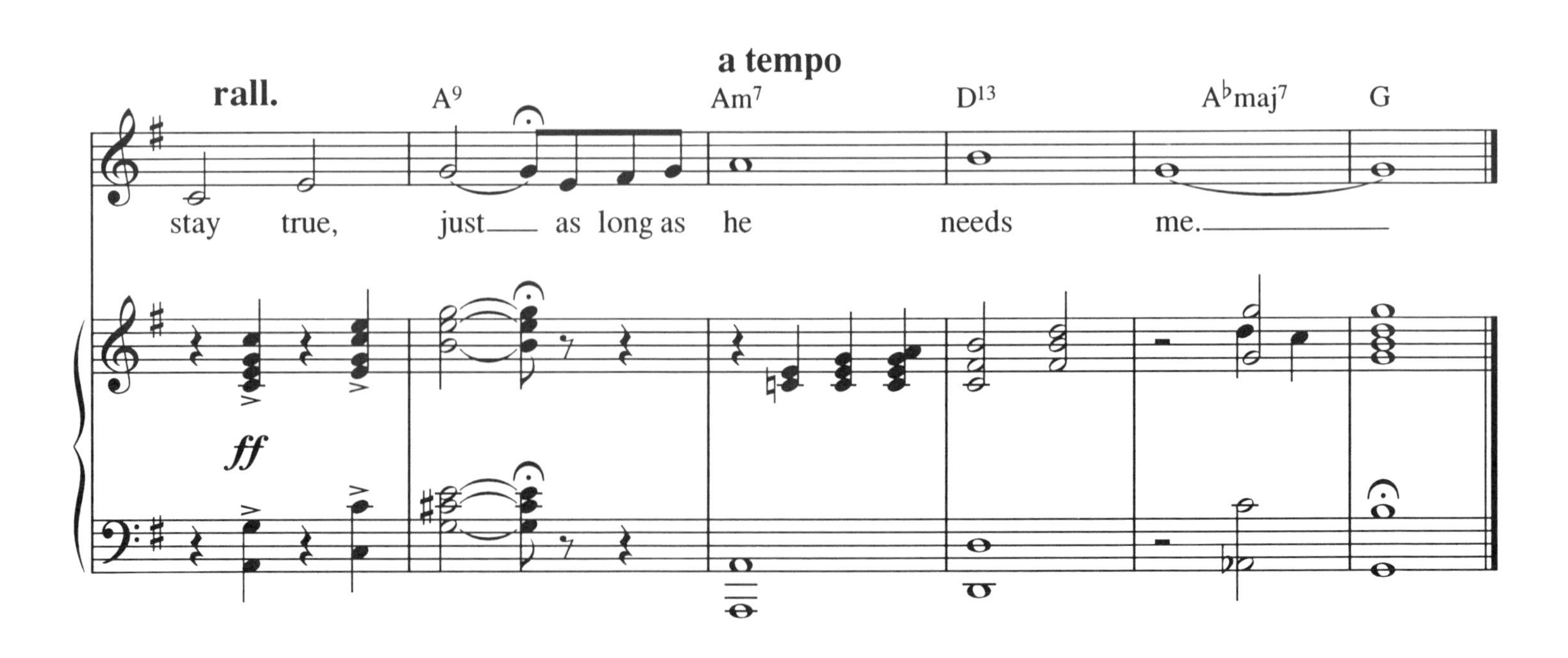
rall.
a tempo
A9
Am7
D13
A♭maj7
G
stay true, just as long as he needs me.

Feeling Good

Words & Music by Leslie Bricusse & Anthony Newley

Am
Am/G
Am/F♯
F
Blos - som on the tree you know how I feel. It's a
Am/E
Am/D
Am/C
E7/B
E
new dawn, it's a new day, it's a new life. for
Am/D
E
Am
F/A
me. And I'm feel - ing good.
Am
Am
G
Dra - gon - fly out in the sun,
dim.
mp

F E Am G
— you know what I mean. But-ter-flies all hav - in' fun,
F E C Am
you know what I mean. Sleep in peace when day — is done, —
Fmaj7 D9 C Am
— that's what I mean. — And this old world — is a new world, and a
F Esus E Am Am/G
bold world — for — me. —
cresc.
f

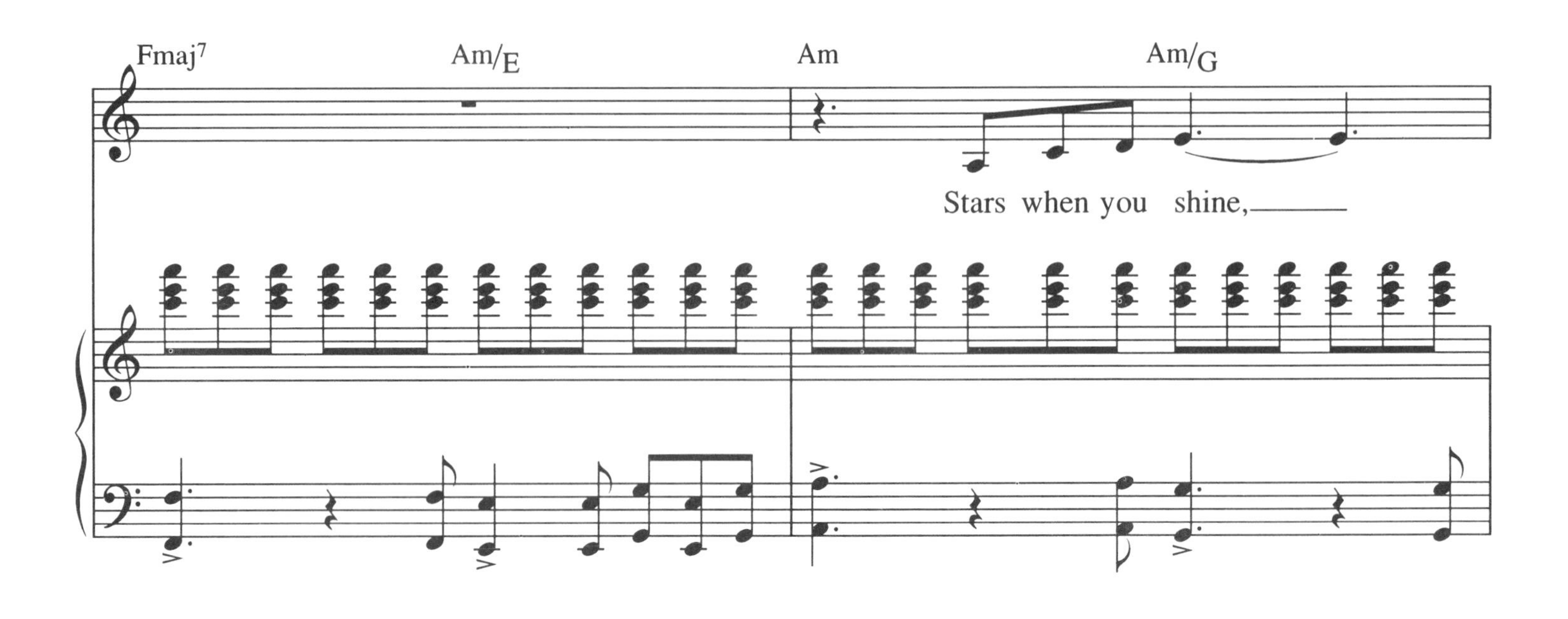
Fmaj7
Am/E
Am
Am/G
Stars when you shine,

F
E7
Am
Am/G
you know how I feel.
Scent of the pine

F
E7
Am
Am/G
— you know how I feel.
Free - dom is mine,

Am/F♯
F
Am/E
Am/D
and I know how I feel.
It's a new dawn, it's a new day, it's a
poco rall.
Am/C
E7/B
E
D9
Esus
new life
for
me.
I'm feel-ing
good.
Am
Am/G
Am/F♯
F
Am/E
Am/D
Am/C
E7/B
E
Am

I Say A Little Prayer

Words by Hal David
Music by Burt Bacharach

D C♯ F♯m
say a lit-tle prayer for you.
While comb-ing my
Bm7 E Aadd9
hair now, and won-d'ring what dress to wear now, I
D C♯ D E9
say a lit-tle prayer for you.
For-ev-er for-ev-er you'll
f
C♯m7 F♯m7 G A A9 D E9
stay in my heart and I will love you for-ev-er and ev-er we

C♯m7 F♯m7 D/F♯ F♯m7 G/A A D E9
never will part, oh how I'll love you, to-geth-er, to-geth-er, that's
C♯m7 F♯m7 G A A9 D D6
how it must be. To live with-out you would on-ly mean heart-break for
1. C♯ 2. C♯ F♯m
me. me. My dar-ling be-
dim.
dim.
mf
Bm7 D/E
-lieve me, for me there is no-one but

Verse 2:
I run for the bus, dear;
While riding, I think of us dear.
I say a little prayer for you.
At work I just take time,
And all through my coffee break time
I say a little prayer for you.

Forever, forever, *etc.*

I Don't Know How To Love Him

Music by Andrew Lloyd Webber
Lyrics by Tim Rice

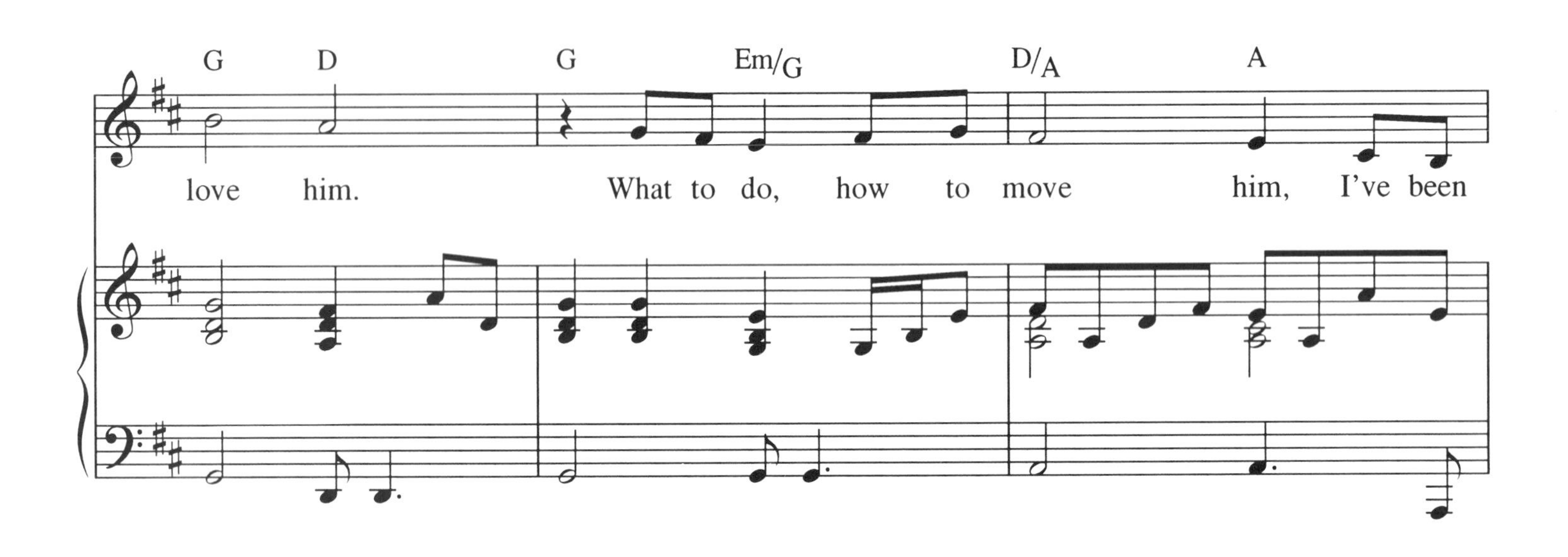

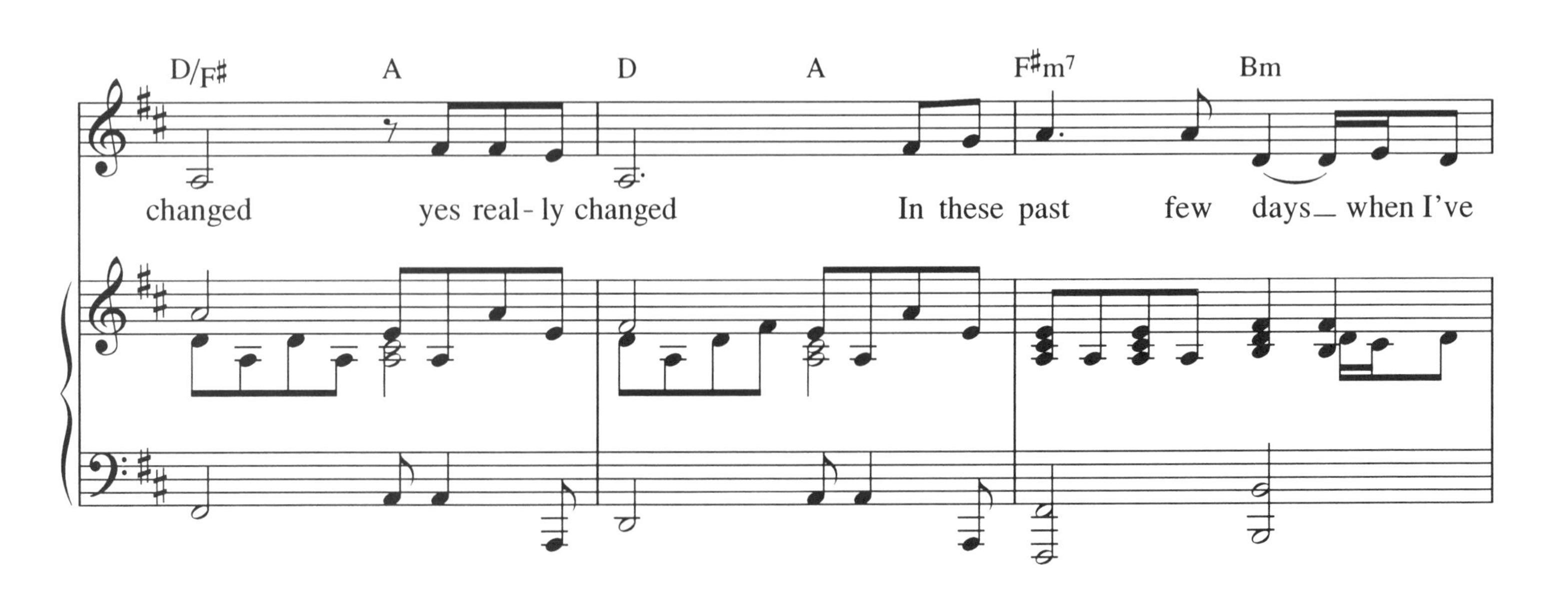

F♯m7 Bm G D/F♯ Em D Em7/A A
seen my - self I seem like some - one else
D G D G D G
I don't know how to take this I don't see why he
D/A A D/F♯ A D A
moves me, He's a man he's just a man And I've
F♯m7 Bm F♯m7 Bm G D/F♯ Em D
had so ma - ny men be - fore in ve - ry ma - ny

Em7/A A G D/F♯ Em D G
ways He's just one more. Should I bring him down,
mf
F♯7 Bm Bm/A G
should I scream and shout, Should I speak of love let my feel-ings out?
D/A C G D G D/F♯
I ne-ver thought I'd come to this what's it all a-
Em G/A A G/A A D G D
-bout? Don't you think it's ra-ther
Yet if he said he
mp

G D G D/A A
fun - ny I should be in this po - si - - tion? I'm the
loved me I'd be lost I'd be fright - - ened I could - n't
D/F♯ A D A F♯m7 Bm
one who's al - ways been So calm so cool
cope just could - n't cope I'd turn my head
To Coda
F♯m7 Bm G D/F♯ Em D Em7/A A G D/F♯ Em7
no lo - ver's fool Run - ning ev - 'ry show He scares me
I'd back a - way I would - n't want to know He scares me
D G F♯7
so.
so.
mf
cresc.

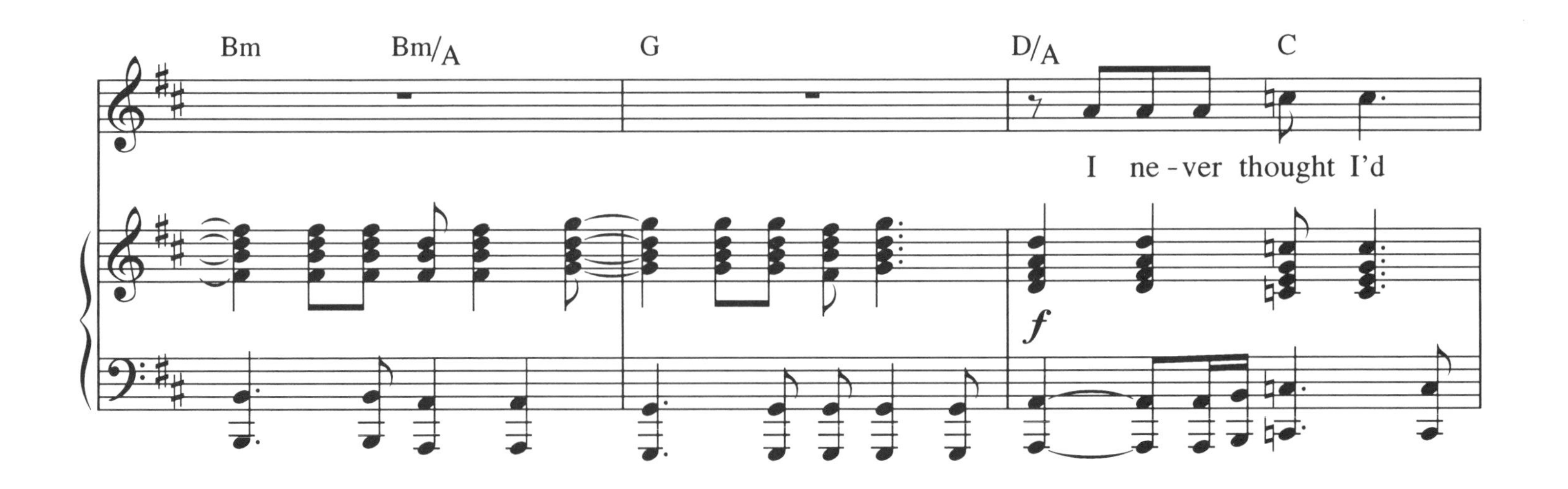
Bm
Bm/A
G
D/A
C
I ne-ver thought I'd

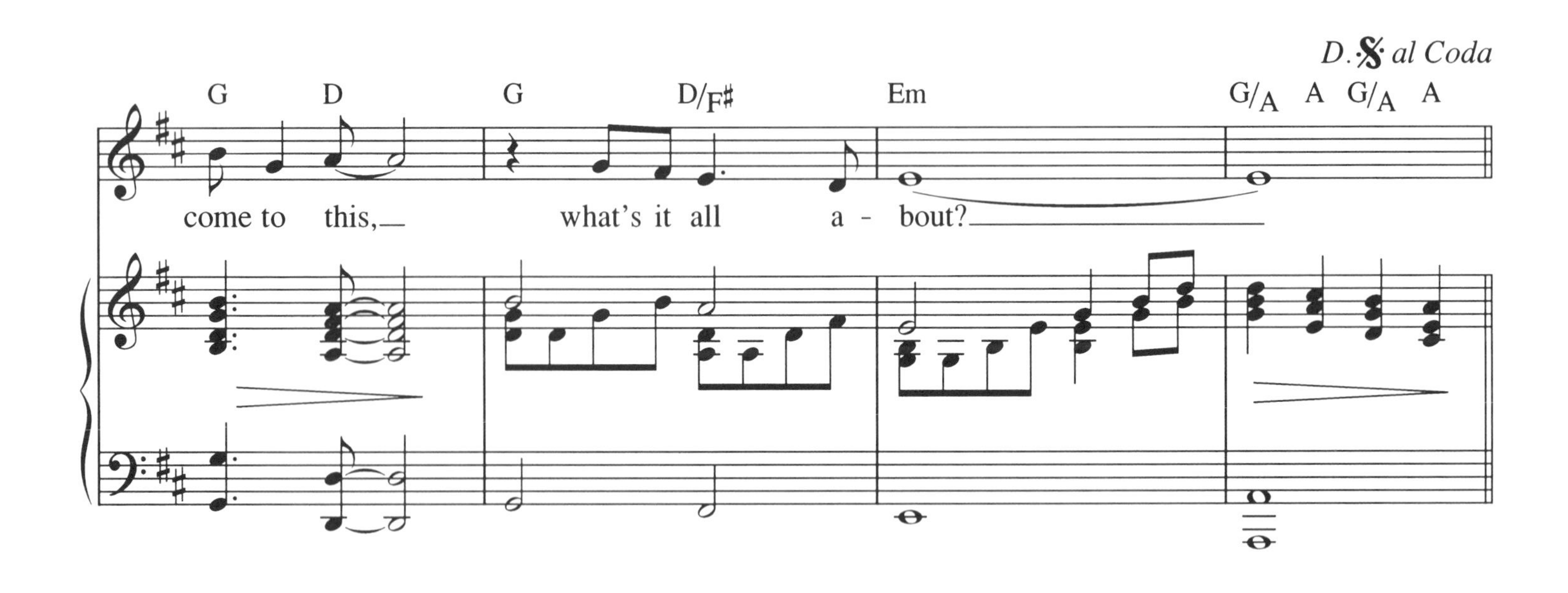
D.𝄋 al Coda
G
D
G
D/F♯
Em
G/A A G/A A
come to this,
what's it all a - bout?

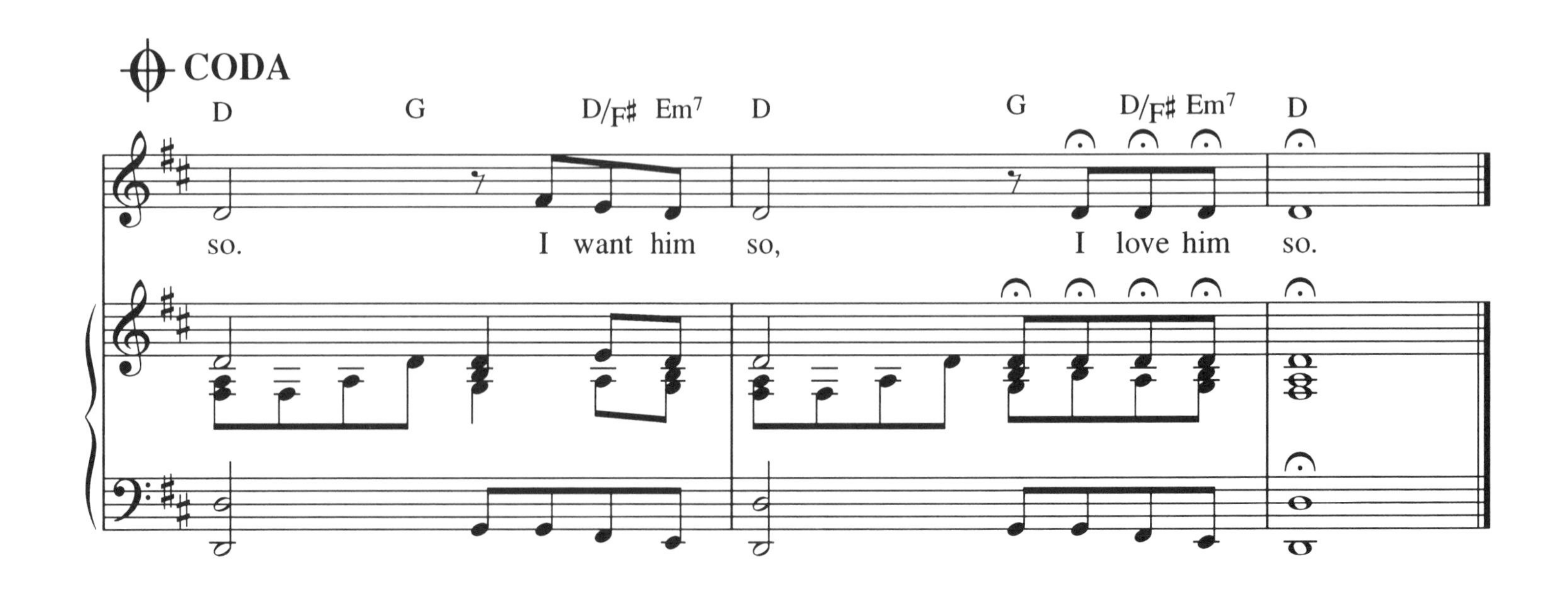
CODA
D
G
D/F♯ Em7
D
G
D/F♯ Em7
D
so.
I want him so,
I love him so.

If My Friends Could See Me Now

Words by Dorothy Fields
Music by Cy Coleman

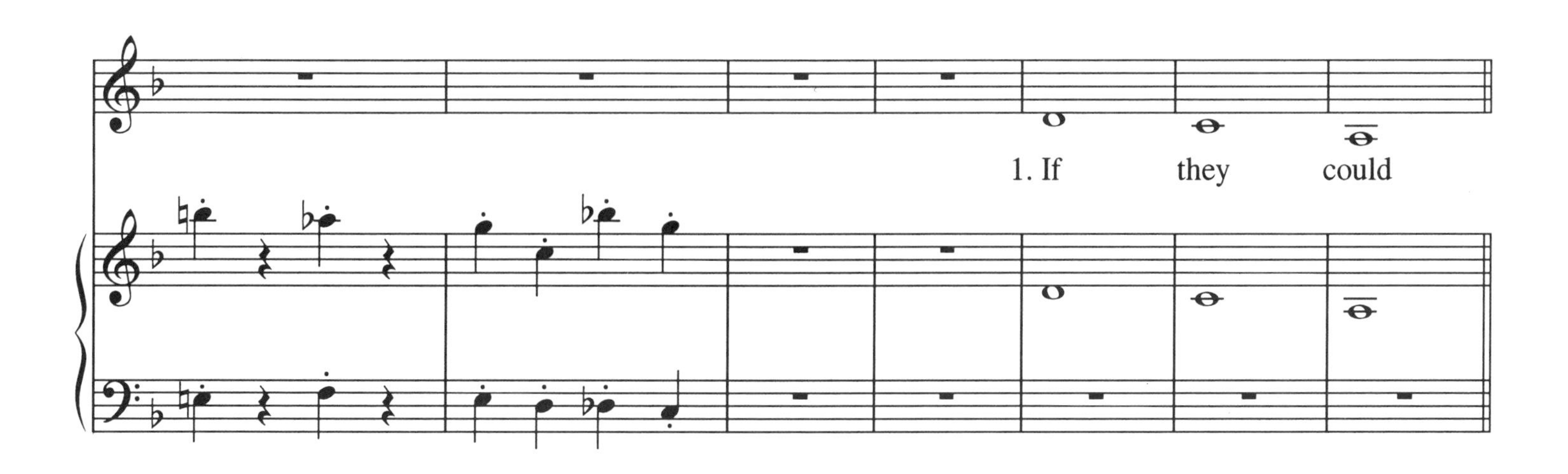

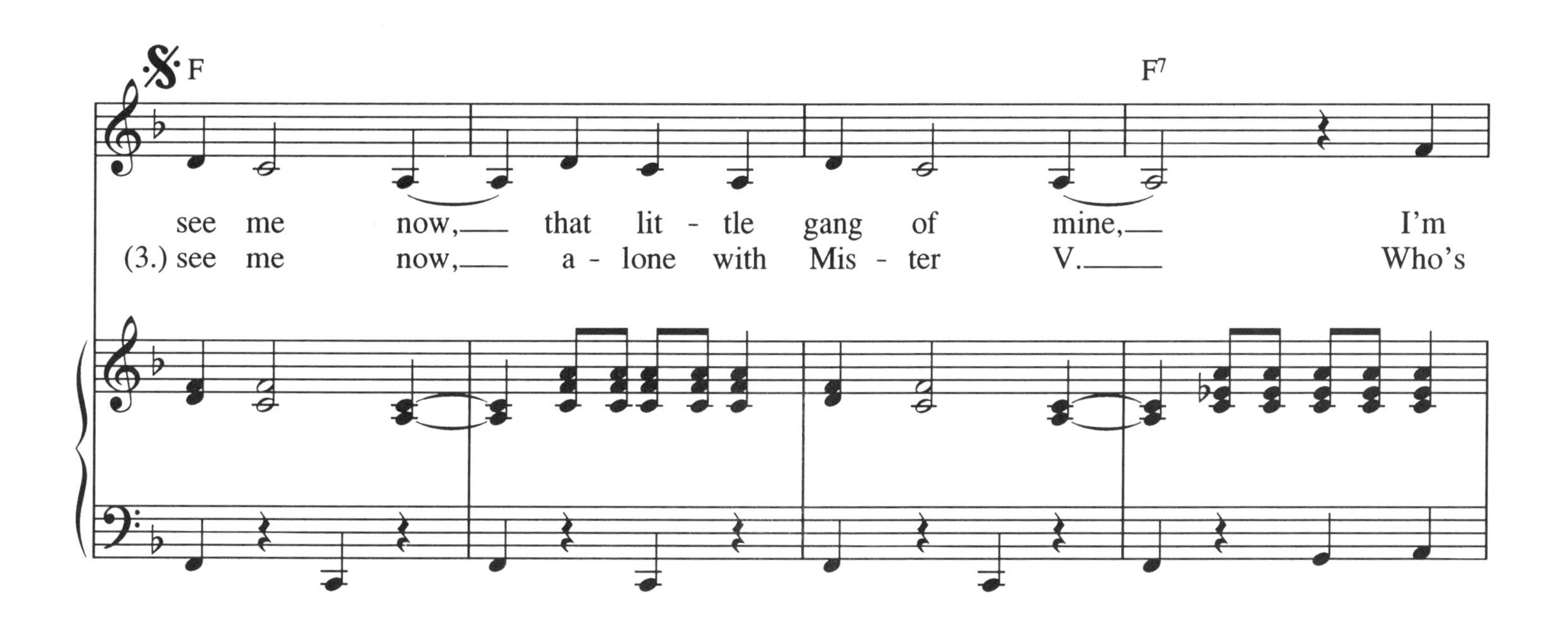

B♭6
eat - ing fan - cy chow and drink- ing fan - cy wine. I'd like those
wait - in' on me like he was a mai - tre d'. I hear my

E F♯m9 Gdim E/G♯ A7 Dm
stum - ble bums to see for a fact the kind of
bud - dies say - ing, "Cra - zy, what gives? To - night she's

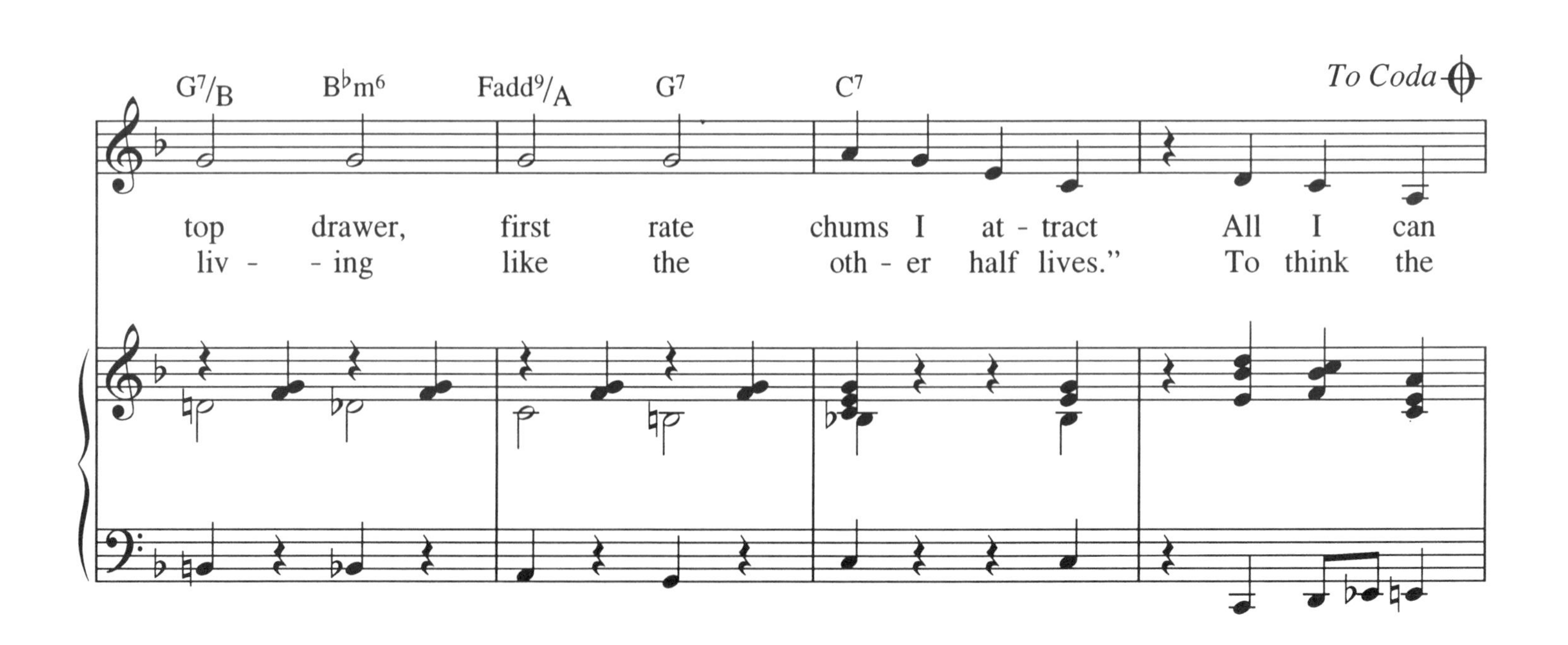
G7/B B♭m6 Fadd9/A G7 C7
To Coda
top drawer, first rate chums I at - tract All I can
liv - - ing like the oth - er half lives." To think the

F
F7
say is Wow - ee! Look - a where I am, to - night I
B♭6
A7
land - ed pow! Right in a pot of jam." What a
Daug
E♭maj7
Em7(♭5)
D7/F♯
G
set up! Ho - ly cow! They'd nev - er be - lieve it, if my
C13
D♭dim
Dm7
C7/E
F
N.C.
friends could see me now.

2. If they could
F6/9
see me now, my lit - tle dust - y group,
mp

B♭6/9
traip - sin' round this mil - lion dol - lar chick - en coop. I'd hear those
E7
A
thrift shop cats say, "Bro - ther, get her! Draped on a
G7
C7
bed - spread made from three kinds of fur." All I can
F6/9
F9
say is Wow! Wait till the riff and raff see just ex -

B♭6/9
A7
-act - ly how he signed this au - to - - graph." What a
Daug E♭maj7 Em7(♭5) D7/F♯ G N.C.
build up! Ho - ly cow! They'd nev - er be - lieve it, if my
mf
C13 D♭dim Dm7 C7/E N.C.
friends could see me now.
D.𝄋 al Coda
3. If they could

CODA
F6/9
high - est brow which I must say is he should pick the
mp
B♭6/9
A7
low - est brow which there's no doubt is me. What a
D7
E♭7
E7
D/F♯
G
Am11
B♭dim
G/B
step up! Ho - ly cow! They'd nev-er be - lieve it if my
f
C13
D♭dim
B♭maj/D
C7/E
F
friends could see me now.

It's Oh So Quiet

Words & Music by Hans Lang, Bert Reisfeld & Erich Meder

Medium swing
B♭7
B♭7(♯9)
E♭9
A♭
B♭m9
peace - ful un - til
You fall in love, zing boom.
f
A♭6/C
D♭6
B♭7/D
E♭
E9(♯11)
E♭
C7
The sky up a - bove, zing boom, is cav - ing in,
1.
B♭7
D♭dim
F13
B♭7
wow bam. You've ne - ver been so nuts a - bout a guy: you
mf
B9(♭5)
F9(♭5)
wan - na laugh you wan - na cry; you cross your heart and hope to die

Tempo I
2.
B♭add9
F
B13
B♭13
'til it's ov - er. And
wow bam, of fall - ing in
ff
Tempo I
E♭
Gm/D
A♭/C
B♭
E♭
love?
mp
Gm/D
B♭
E♭
Gm/D
It's oh so quiet,
E♭6
Gm7
G♭dim
B♭7/F
Edim
B♭7/F
it's oh so still.
You're
8va

B♭
B9(♯11)
B♭7
all a - lone and so peace - ful un -
(8)
loco
Tempo 2
E♭
B♭7(♯9)
E♭9
A♭
B♭m9
A♭6/C
D♭6
B♭7/D
- til You blow a fuse, zing boom; the de - vil cuts
f
E♭
E9(♯11)
E♭
C7
F
B13
B♭13
loose, zing boom. So what's the use, wow bam, of fall - ing in love?
E♭6/9
D♭6/9
E♭6
Fm9
The sky caves in, the

Verse 2:
And then it's nice and quiet.
But soon again starts another big riot.
You blow a fuse, zing boom,
The devil cuts loose, zing boom.
So what's the use, wow bam,
Of falling in love?

Killing Me Softly With His Song

Words by Norman Gimbel
Music by Charles Fox

Fm
B♭m7
E♭7
Strum-ming my pain with his fin - gers,
sing-ing my life with his words.
(♭)
A♭
Fm
B♭/D
Kill-ing me soft - ly with his song, kill-ing me soft -
E♭
D♭
A♭
- ly with his song, tell-ing my whole life with his
D♭
G♭
To Coda
F
1.2.
words, kill-ing me soft - ly with his song.

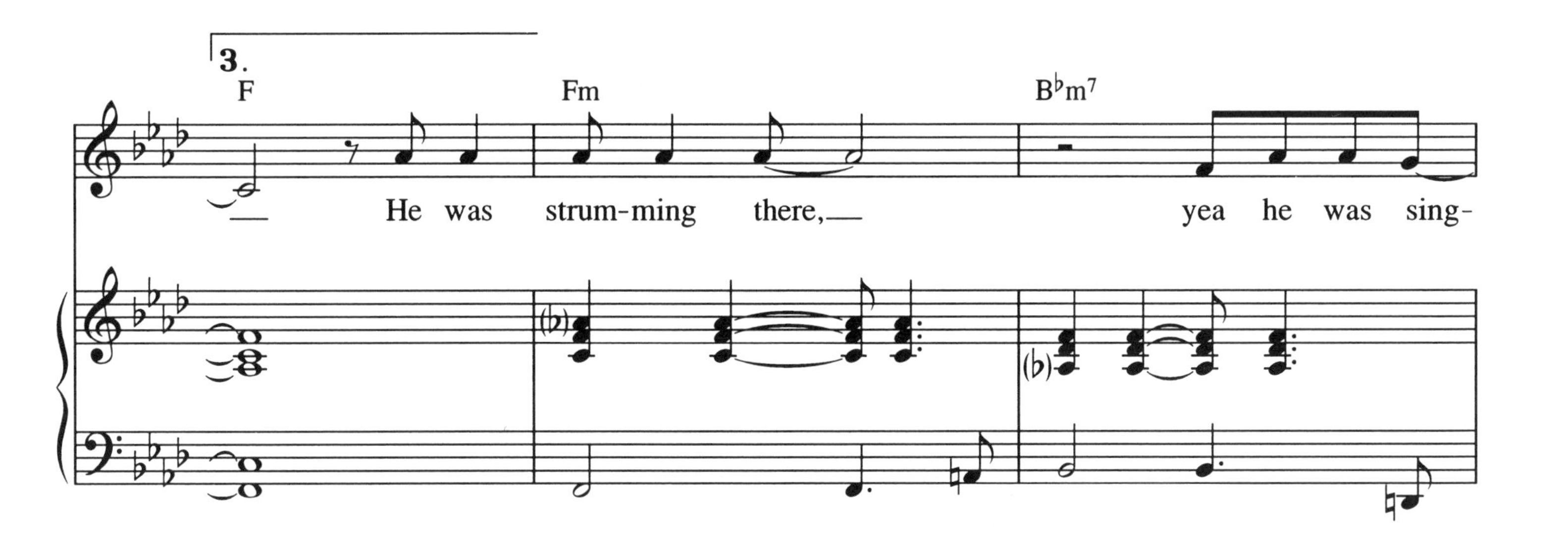

Verse 2:
I felt all flushed with fever,
Embarrassed by the crowd.
I felt he found my letters
And read each one out loud.
I prayed that he would finish,
But he just kept right on.

Strumming my pain *etc.*

Verse 3:
He sang as if he knew me
In all my dark despair.
And then he looked right through me
As if I wasn't there.
But he was there this stranger,
Singing clear and strong.

Strumming my pain *etc.*

Tell Me It's Not True

Words & Music by Willy Russell

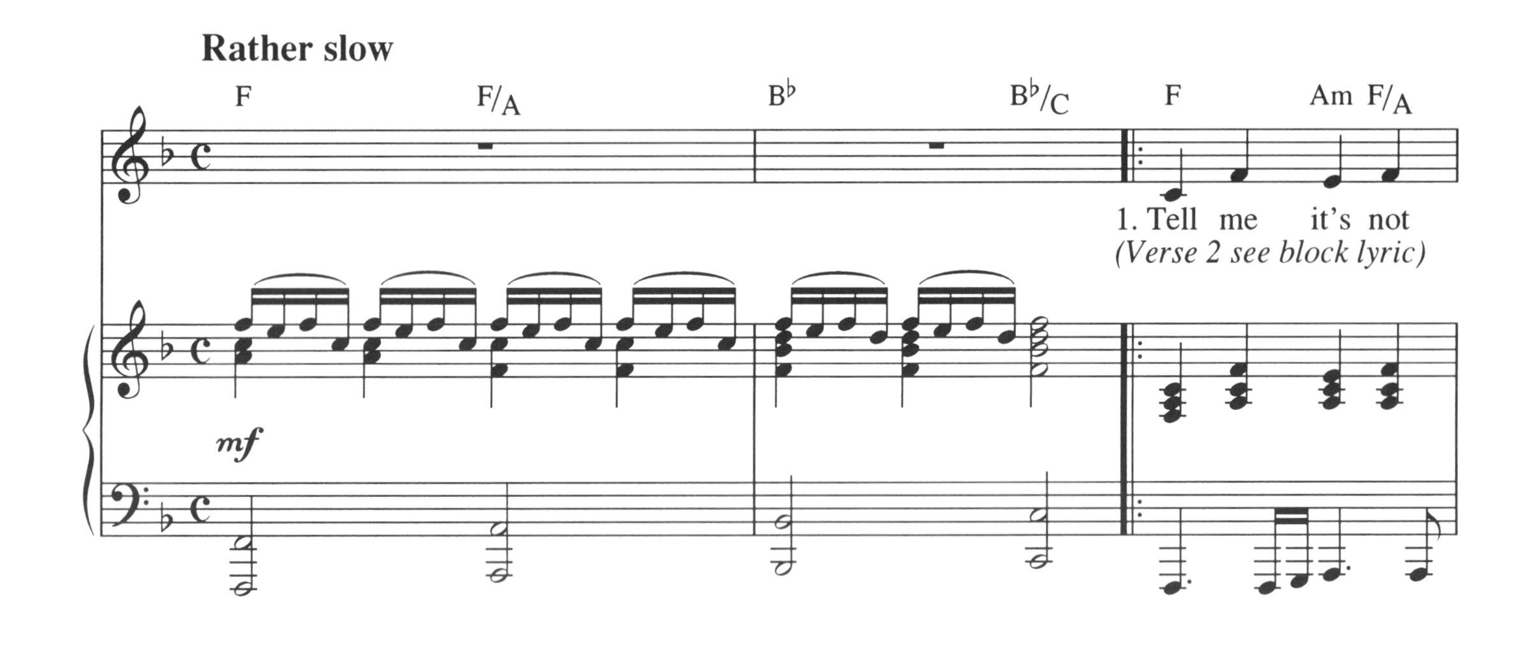

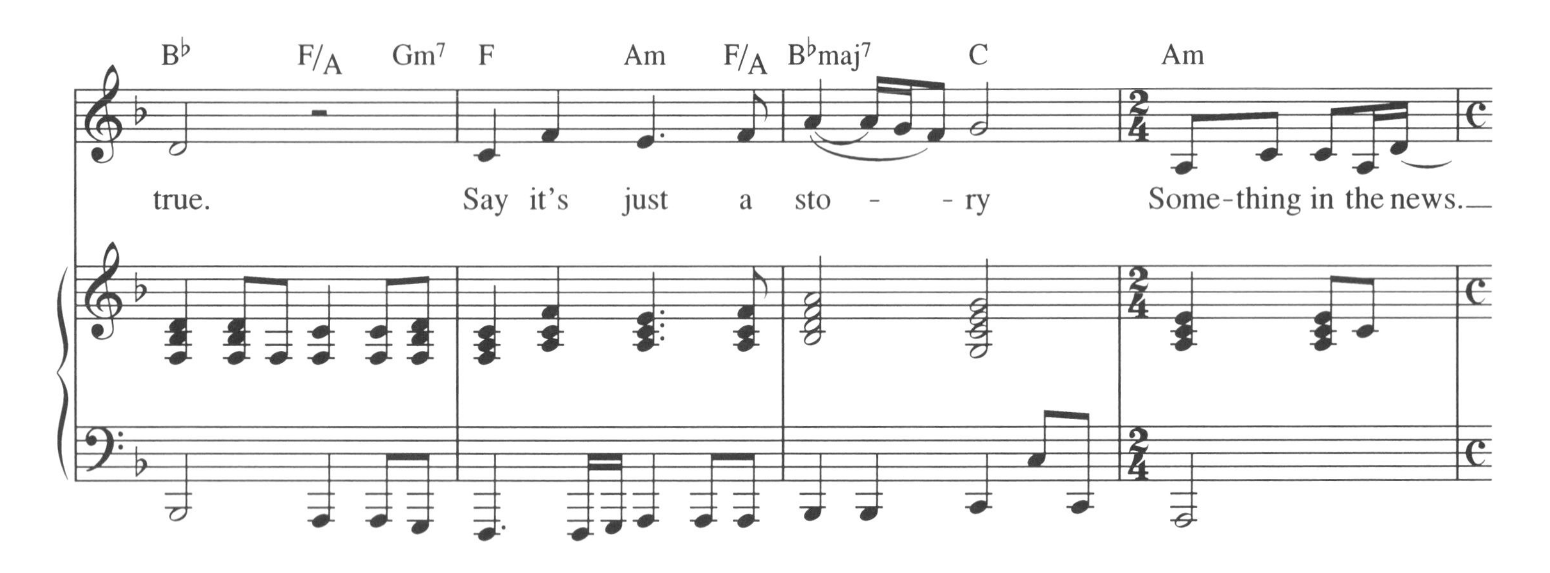

B♭maj7 C Am Dm C/E F
-fore me. Say it's just a dream, say it's just a scene
F C/E F B♭ F/A Gm F C F C/E F B♭ F/A
from an old mo-vie of years a - go; from an old mo-vie of
Gm F C B♭/C
Ma-ri-lyn Mon - roe.
F Am F/A B♭ F/A Gm7
Tell me it's not true.
f

F Am F/A B♭maj7 C
Say I on - - ly dreamed it. And
Am B♭ F/A Gm7 F Am F/A
morn - ing will come soon. Tell me it's not
B♭ F/A Gm7 F Am F/A
true. Say you did - - n't
B♭maj7 C Am Dm
mean it. Say it's just pre - tend,

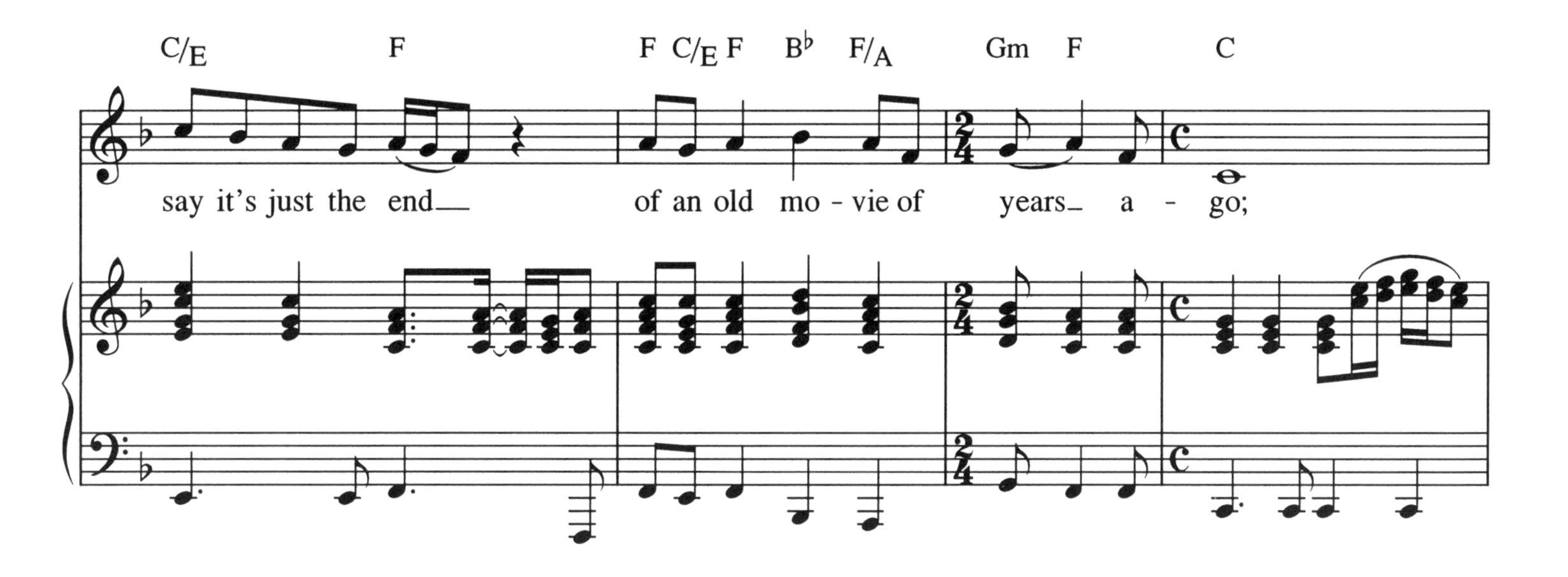

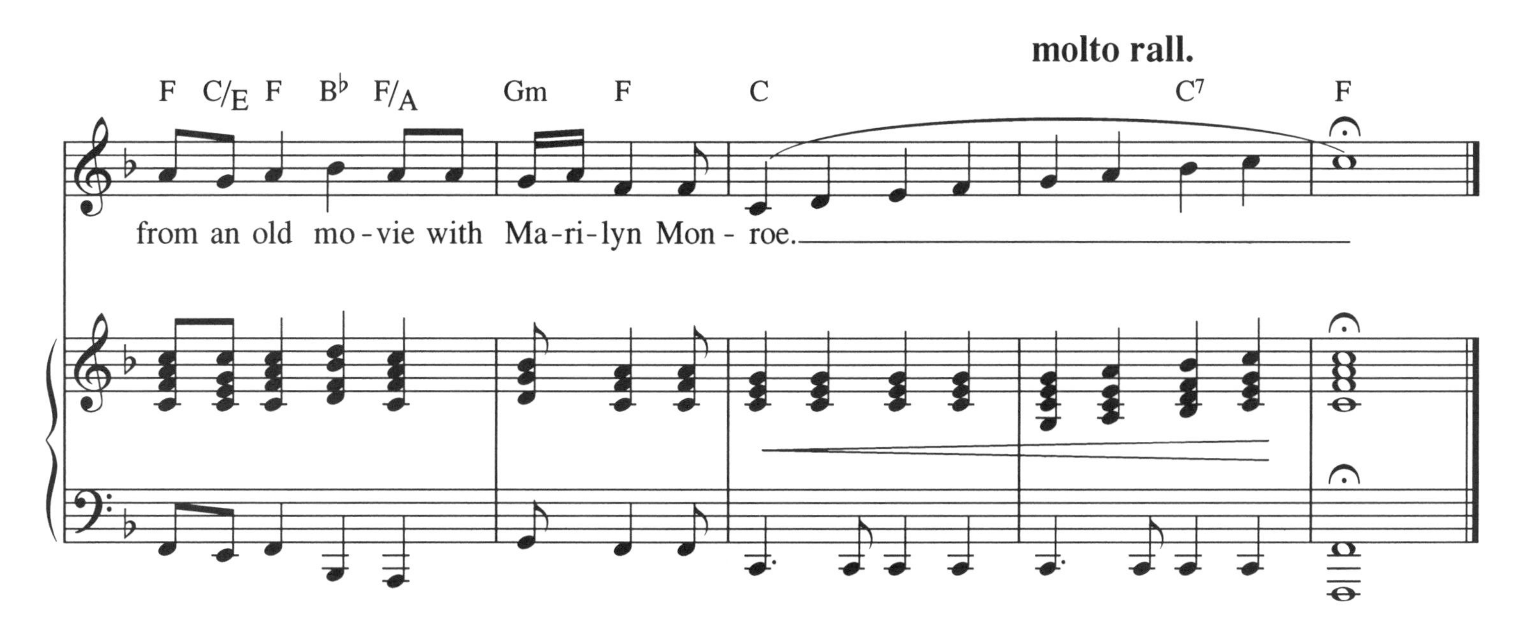

Verse 2:
Say it's just some clowns,
Two players in the limelight.
And bring the curtain down.
Say it's just two clowns
Who couldn't get their lines right.
Say it's just a show on the radio
That we can turn over and start again;
We can turn over, it's only a game.

You Must Love Me

Music by Andrew Lloyd Webber
Lyrics by Tim Rice

C7 F F/E Dm7
what do we do for our dream to sur-vive, how do we keep all our
F/G G F/G G
pas-sions a - live as we used to do?
cresc.
E7 Am E7
Deep in my heart I'm con - ceal - ing things that I'm long-ing to
Am E7 G/F F
say, scared to con-fess what I'm feel - ing
ten.
dim.

Verse 2:
Why are you at my side?
How can I be any use to you now?
Give me a chance and I'll let you see how
Nothing has changed.
Deep in my heart I'm concealing
Things that I'm longing to say,
Scared to confess what I'm feeling
Frightened you'll slip away,
You must love me.

3/01 (39750)
Printed in England by Caligraving Limited Thetford Norfolk